Science
and Creation
An Introduction
to Some Tough Issues

Wayne Frair

Illustrated by Andrea Reekstin

Creation Research Society
Reader Series: No. 3

Creation Research Society Books
2002

Science and Creation:
An Introduction to Some Tough Issues

by Wayne Frair

Illustrated by Andrea Reekstin

Design by Cindy Blandon

Cover photograph at Lake Stanley, Stanley, Idaho,
by Glen W. Wolfrom

ISBN 0-940384-25-6

Printed in the United States of America

*This book is dedicated to those who
are searching for truth about science
and origins in a confused world.*

Contents

Preface

It is a joy and an honor to produce a Preface for this volume written by my friend of many years, Dr. Wayne Frair. Its title is *Science and Creation: An Introduction to Some Tough Issues*. Let us study that title closely and take a closer look at its author as well.

Since the first title word is *Science*, it would be ideal if the writer had a deep understanding of that field. He would be even more adequately prepared for the task if he were a *practicing* scientist. Four earned degrees in science, decades of teaching, and avid reading all have provided Dr. Frair with a thorough scientific knowledge. For many years he also has conducted field and laboratory studies of his own on turtles, especially immunochemistry as applied to their classification or taxonomy. Published reports of his findings have appeared in such journals as *Science* and the *Journal of Herpetology*, which have worldwide readership. He works with precisely the right kind of credentials and background when he develops the definition, history, and limits of science in this book.

Word number three in the title is *Creation* which is the belief that there is a Creator who worked directly and rapidly to synthesize all of what is called "nature." Creationists hold many beliefs about *how* God did His creation work. One of these is that various plants and animals as well as people were created separately from each other according to many different "kinds," as the Bible says, and that they did not all just "evolve" from one common ancestry. In other words, they all came from the same Creator, but not from the same ancestry. Someone who produces a hybrid book about "Science *and* Creation" had better be a scientist who really believes in creation and can expound on it too.

Wayne Frair has been an avid scholar of creation and has written many papers and books on that theme. The Creation Research Society (CRS) is an assemblage of scientific creationists who print the results of their investigations in the *Creation Research Society Quarterly (CRSQ)*. Dr. Frair has been active as a member, a writer, and a Board officer in the CRS since its early years. He has taken his stand for creation out to the scientific public, as well, by promoting creation literature at national meetings. He is a fellow of the American Association for the Advancement of Science. He has delivered many open lectures on creation topics, and in 1981 appeared as an expert witness at the famous Arkansas Creation Trial. Also his agenda has included the introducing of librarians to scholarly creation books. During recent years Wayne Frair has been participating with other scientists in a "Baraminology Study Group" having the purpose of analyzing and classifying forms of life from a discontinuity perspective. Please trust me when I assert that Dr. Frair capably has communicated the history, meaning, and importance of creation in the pages of this present book.

Finally, the book's subtitle reads: *An Introduction to Some Tough Issues*. As a prerequisite to covering science and creation, a thorough scholar would need to explore other complex matters such as philosophy, religion, faith, and theology. If all of these fields of discussion were defined, simplified and clarified, the reader would be doubly rewarded. You will discover that Dr. Frair has accomplished all of this and more. Andrea Reekstin, the talented illustrator of the book, has inserted yet another dimension, helping to illuminate the "tough issues" of origins. Using this book, both novices and veterans, young and old alike, will be able to establish a solid foundation for further studies. Those who already are well-versed in creation science will find the treatise valuable in organizing and integrating their own ideas. Let me be the first to welcome *Science and Creation: An Introduction to Some Tough Issues* to its well-deserved place within our CRS series of short volumes on creation science.

George F. Howe, Ph.D.
Editor of the *Creation Research Society Quarterly*
Retired College Professor of Biology

Acknowledgments

This entire manuscript in two drafts was read thoroughly by George Howe who made countless valuable suggestions. Editor Michael J. Oard helpfully has been engaged throughout the processes of preparation and production; and his wife, Beverly Oard, as a reader, has rendered many constructive criticisms. Others who helpfully have reviewed a copy of the entire manuscript include Brian Bell, Eugene F. Chaffin, Donald B. DeYoung, William Theodore Snyder, and Rebecca Wolfrom. Emmett L. Williams not only helped improve the whole document but also contributed his expertise setting up the writing in final form. My wife, Elizabeth Frair, and many other friends have supported and contributed significantly. Illustrator Andrea Reekstin graciously volunteered her very valuable time and expertise, and graphic designer Cindy Blandon meticulously prepared the entire document for publication.

.

Introduction

Science in itself is an exciting enterprise, but when the student of nature is tuned to the Creator, his or her personal life is fulfilled. Then the studies of our surroundings, and even of ourselves, have a richness which is unattainable by those who reach no farther than the physical universe. It is the purpose of this book to explore some vital issues in science, theology, faith, and creation from both historic and twenty-first-century perspectives. The text is designed for those in early stages of scientific studies and for those with a somewhat stronger scientific training lacking in theological perspectives. It is the author's hope that all readers will be encouraged to probe more deeply into the issues presented.

1

Science and Christian Belief

What is Science?

All of us have heard and used the word science, but do we have a good basic understanding of what it really is? To different people the word "science" conjures up so many ideas that it often is difficult to obtain a clear definition of the word. It comes from the Latin *scire* which means "to know," and so science can be defined as knowledge. However, knowledge is too general a definition, because when we talk about science we almost always are referring to the whole of nature. Nature means anything in the universe such as stars, trees, animals, rocks, and air. Actually, anything we can detect by our five senses of touch, taste, sight, smell, and hearing is part of nature. Often instruments like telescopes, microscopes, spectrophotometers, and computers are utilized to aid our senses and enhance our knowledge and understanding of nature.

Science which deals with nature usually is called *natural science,* for example astronomy, biology, chemistry, and physics. But there also is *social science* which includes sociology and psychology. Even *theology* may be approached from a scientific perspective. Some scholars, particularly in past years, have considered theology to be the "Queen" of the sciences.

Scientific Method

A second and more popular definition of the word science focuses on what is done by those who perform scientific activities. Scientists follow a procedure known as the *scientific method.* In its essence, the scientific method involves collecting *facts (perceptions),* drawing *conclusions,* and then *testing* what has been concluded. Also, it often is possible to *predict* future findings on the basis of what has been discovered. The earliest form of a conclusion is termed a *hypothesis,* and if this hypothesis is confirmed by testing, it then becomes a *theory.* After further extensive confirmation, the theory becomes a *law* (see Figure 1).

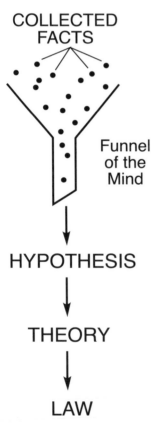

Figure 1. The scientific method involves collecting facts and making conclusions based on the facts. The first conclusion is termed a hypothesis. When the hypothesis is tested and confirmed, the conclusion is called a theory, and after repeated confirmation, the theory becomes a law.

An example of a scientific "law" is Newton's law of gravity which states that bodies are attracted toward each other, the heavier object exerting a stronger attracting force than does the lighter one. The law of biogenesis states that all forms of life come only from the same types of life as illustrated in Figure 2.

One very fundamental law of *science* is called the first law of thermodynamics which says that matter (the stuff of nature) or energy (the ability or capacity to do work) neither can be created nor destroyed. Matter can be converted to energy, and energy can

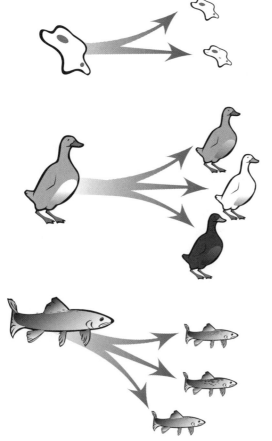

Figure 2. Law of Biogenesis. This is a well-established concept in science. Every type of living thing produces offspring of the same type with some possible slight variations.

Figure 3. Matter may be converted to energy and energy to matter. But matter/energy can neither be created nor destroyed, only transformed. This is the first law of thermodynamics.

change into matter as illustrated in Figure 3. There are no known exceptions.

These processes are only transformations (not creations) since neither matter nor energy can be created or destroyed. A very important implication of the first law of thermodynamics is that nature consisting of matter and energy could not have created itself. A power beyond nature (or *super*natural power) was necessary to do this. This will be discussed in more detail later.

What is Theology?

Theology comes from the Greek referring to God, and theology can be defined as the study of God as related to nature, that is, the creation. God is the supernatural (beyond nature) power who was necessary at the beginning to bring nature into existence, since nature could not have created itself.

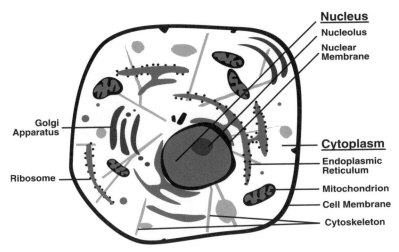

Figure 4. A cell—evidence of intelligent design. All living things are composed of cells and the products of cells. This is a law of biology. The human body consists of about ten trillion cells. One hundred years ago scientists thought that a cell was very simple— like a blob of jelly; but now continuing studies of cells keep yielding more details about their intricacy, which is evidence for intelligent design.

Information about God is received by revelation. One form of revelation is termed *natural revelation,* wherein God is revealed when a person observes some aspect of nature. When someone looks at the sky and perceives the grandeur of the stars, this awesome sight points the person to a power that transcends the whole universe. The Bible refers to this in Psalm 19:1 where it states that "The heavens declare the glory of God."

Not only is God revealed by heavenly bodies we can observe, but also He is revealed in a multitude of other aspects of nature, such as the intricacy of plant and animal design, for example. When using high magnification to examine the inside of the cells which compose all living organisms we can recognize evidence of intelligent design. See Figure 4. In Romans 1:20 the Bible says, "For since the creation of the world God's invisible qualities—his eternal power and divine nature—have been clearly seen, being understood from what has been made, so that men are without excuse." So all people have an obligation to acknowledge and respond to this God who reveals Himself in nature.

Intelligent Design

The argument for *intelligent design* can be made on the basis of *universal human experience*. For example, when people find arrowheads or other carvings, like faces on Mount Rushmore in

Figure 5. On the left is a crude natural rock formation (Old Man of the Mountain) on Cannon Mountain in New Hampshire. On the right is the face of Abraham Lincoln carved on the side of Mount Rushmore in South Dakota. We easily can recognize that one is a natural formation and the other the result of intelligent design and carving.

South Dakota (Figure 5), they easily can recognize these as objects of human design and construction. The same reasoning extends to automobiles, to buildings of all sorts, and to computers. Objects with such organization and parts with useful purposes do not come into existence by "natural" processes, but rather only by intelligent design and intelligent construction (human creations).

Peoples in *all* cultures, past and present, likewise have recognized this design as pointing to a supernatural Creator God. This is an inescapable conclusion based upon all available evidence. There are great differences among peoples of different cultures living at a multitude of locations all over the surface of planet earth. But in *all* of these groups there is a belief in a Power beyond nature which is clear evidence that recognition of the Supernatural is a universal human attribute—Figure 6. Also, people want to know and to communicate with this "God" and to experience the very best God has for their lives.

Many scholars have recognized that there must be a supernatural God to satisfy these basic human desires, because men and women of every tribe and nation have them. There are means to satisfy other basic human needs like food for hunger, air for breathing, and water for thirst. Without food, air, and water, a person will die. Therefore God must exist to satisfy the universal basic spiritual hunger or thirst that all peoples have. The Bible says that those who deny God His rightful place in their lives are spiritually dead, but they can become alive by a spiritual rebirth. Hundreds of years ago Augustine made the wise statement that people have been created with an empty place in their lives—a place that only God can fill.

*Figure 6. People in every "uncivilized" and "civilized" culture
exhibit a natural belief in a supernatural power. The lower group of
worshipers is in an "undeveloped" primitive society, whereas the
above gathering is of "cultured" people outside a modern church
building. In both situations the people have come together in
recognition of a supernatural God.*

Belief in God—Logical and Satisfying

Multitudes of people over thousands of years have recognized that belief in God not only is *logical,* but also is *satisfying.* When groups of people or even nations (as done a few years ago in Albania and Russia) have declared atheism to be their religion, this has been like holding a cork under water; see Figure 7. The cork will rise to the top of the water as soon as the pressure is removed from above. So it is with people. When an atheistic pressure is taken off, men and women openly begin to worship God again. Belief in God can only be suppressed, not destroyed.

There also is a variety of formal arguments which philosophers have used over the years in order to demonstrate that belief in God is very logical. For example, events appear to be the result of causes. There is at least one and usually more than one cause for every event (or effect). If somebody becomes sick he or she wants

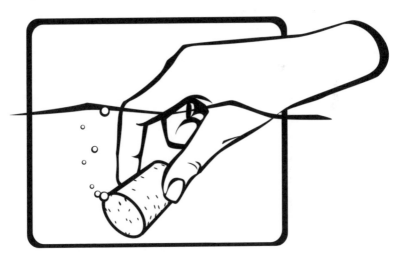

Figure 7. A cork being held down in the water. Cork will float unless something is holding it below the surface of the water. When atheistic governments put pressure on people to reject God and to abandon worship, it is like holding a cork under the water.

to know what is the cause of the sickness (effect). Or, if a man finds a big dent (effect) in the fender of his new car in a parking lot he wants to know what caused the dent.

The whole universe (including our human bodies) basically consists of matter and energy, as was discussed earlier in this book. Matter can be converted to energy and energy can be converted to matter, but, neither matter nor energy can be created or destroyed, according to the first law of thermodynamics. They only can be transformed as illustrated in Figure 3 (p. 18).

If, on a big big scale, we think back over the years, decades, centuries and millenniums, we eventually can come to a first effect and a first cause. Let's consider that there was matter and/or energy in some form. But what was their source? Where did this matter/energy "effect" come from? The source of the matter/energy would be the first, or original, cause. The first law of thermodynamics (matter and energy cannot be created or destroyed) implies that this first cause is outside nature. If this is true, the first cause could not be part of nature but must be *beyond,* or super nature. It is supernatural. We call this supernatural cause "God," who is spirit and is the Creator.

We have been discussing causality, which refers to the reasons for (causes of) something. This approach is basic in scientific activities, for scientists always are seeking the reasons (causes) for this or that. Some scientists (atheists) have avoided the implications of the first law of thermodynamics and said that the universe is eternal, or always has been here. By so doing they abandon their own basic principle of causality and move into the realm of *faith.* Their "faith" is in a self-sustaining eternal universe. In other words, they believe that the universe did not have a cause or beginning.

The line of reasoning that leads to God follows the causal sequence (scientific process) one step beyond that of the atheist (or philosophical naturalist). Since atheists basically express faith in an eternal universe, they stop short of accepting the implications pointing to a supernatural Creator. Yet it is entirely logical to follow the implications that God exists and to have faith in this supernatural Creator God.

Knowing God Personally—What's That?

When we realize that God exists, the next step is to recognize our need to know more about God and what is expected of us in response to what we have learned. Information about the working of God can be understood from *history*, as seen by the judgment that came upon the children of Israel through their exile in the Babylonian captivity (539 B.C.) and during the destruction of Jerusalem in 70 A.D.

Also, our *conscience* prompts us to correct patterns of behavior based on what is morally right or wrong, and these promptings are God-given guidelines. Additionally, necessary revelation comes to us from a book which is the most widely-distributed in the entire world. In it are the Ten Commandments, the Sermon on the Mount, the Gospel of Jesus Christ, and much prophecy about future events. This book commonly is referred to as the *Bible.* It is very reasonable that the Creator would provide an "instruction book." This book reveals information about the Creator, His universe, and how people should live.

It is logical that if such a supernatural Creator God exists, then we as intelligent knowing beings have an obligation to Him. The Bible actually speaks of God as our Father (Deuteronomy 32:6,

Malachi 2:10) because He has created us. We learn further from the New Testament that God is our father in a spiritual sense after we have been "born again" (John 3:3) through belief in His Son, Jesus Christ, as our Lord and Savior.

Are Science and Theology Separate?

The answer to this question is yes, in about the same way that a husband and wife are each a distinct being. However, the lives of both husband and wife overlap in very meaningful ways. In a proper marriage the husband is not independent of his wife, and the wife is not independent of her husband, even though each has some separate roles to play. When you think of one spouse, it

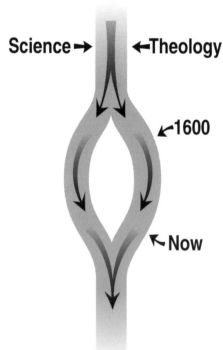

Figure 8. Scientists and theologians considered their fields of study to be closely related until a short time before about 1600 when it started to become more popular to think of them as separate disciplines. Fortunately now there is evidence that the two streams of thought are coming back together. Scientists are discovering that scientific facts imply a supernatural Creator, and theologians are recognizing that scientists are helping them better to understand God's creation.

often is very appropriate to think of the other one also. So it is with science and theology. In considering the Creator, one thinks about nature, which is His creation. When a person considers the universe including the world, its Originator and His sustaining influence come to mind.

Another analogy for thinking about the proper relationship between science and theology (or science and the Bible) is to think about a river. Imagine a line running through the middle of the river dividing it into two portions. We may label the right half of the river "theology" and the left half "science." See the upper part of Figure 8. The water on the far right of this stream is completely separate from the water on the far left. But toward the center region of the river, the water of the right portion intermingles quite intimately with the water immediately to its left. The two streams of thought (theology and science) composing right and left portions of this theoretical river flow together.

Changes in Science

Over the years there have been *many more* changes of thought within fields of science than in theology. For example, 150 years ago scientists accepted the theory that many forms of life were coming from non-living material. But this false idea had been rejected before the beginning of the twentieth century. In 1960, most astronomers believed in the Steady State idea for the origin of the universe, which of course is a major concept. At this same time they also believed in the static positioning of the continents. However, by the middle to late 1960's both of these broad theories largely had been replaced by the Big Bang and that of Continental Drift (plate tectonics) theories respectively, and today there are scientists who are challenging both of these two concepts.

Consequently, as more knowledge accumulates, scientific understanding is modified. So we constantly are dealing with new hypotheses and theories. Occasionally even a law (for example gravity) is modified. So it is important for students of science to keep up with the thinking of scientists about various issues.

In the early decades of the twentieth century scientists were discussing how genetic information could be carried. As time passed, the genetic material came to be associated with chromosomes in the nucleus of a cell and with nucleic acids (DNA and RNA). The basic structure of nucleic acid was reported in 1953, and after that time there has been an explosive expansion of research on genetics.

Now the genes themselves which carry particular genetic information are being modified in laboratories. But at the same time scientists are recognizing that DNA in the genes is not the only substance regulating the structure and function of plants and animals. An increasing intricacy is being discovered, and this involves complicated interactions among proteins, DNA and RNA, as well as other cellular components.

Changes in Theology

Theology includes a study of the relations between God and people, and there have been only such modifications in this relationship as have been given to us by successive revelation in the Bible. God always has expressed His love toward the humans He created. Likewise He has demonstrated His justice and mercy in many ways (for example, Old Testament history).

About 2,000 years ago He sent His Son to die on the cross for the sins of the World (John 1:29). Belief in the basic doctrines of the many denominations of the Christian Church, as expressed in the Apostles' Creed and other Creeds, has not changed in nearly 2,000 years. This is because the basic nature of people and the nature of God have not changed.

Does this mean that theologians in the Christian church should neglect to keep up with what is going on in science? Just as tens of thousands of scientists today are active Christians who endeavor to live according to the Bible, so the specialists (theologians) on the Bible need to keep informed about what is going on in scientific circles. This is true especially where there are issues such as genetic engineering that may affect the philosophy and morality of the society.

Science and Theology Working Together

Somewhat before about 1600 A.D. the theological and scientific streams of thought largely flowed together as illustrated in Figure 8 (p. 26). Back then the mainline scientists saw their work as the gaining of an understanding of what God had created. But the two streams of thought had started and then continued to separate more widely as some scientists became increasingly uncomfortable about discussing theology and science together. Unfortunately, at the present time a number of scientists still retain this attitude.

Arthur Koestler has said that the separation of science and theology has caused an impoverishment of both of these fields.[1] Fortunately, there now is evidence that the streams of thought are coming back together. In 1978 astronomer Robert Jastrow said:

> For the scientist who has lived by his faith in the power of reason, the story ends like a bad dream. He has scaled the

mountains of ignorance; he is about to conquer the highest peak; as he pulls himself over the final rock, he is greeted by a band of theologians who have been sitting there for centuries.[2]

There was predictive power in this famous statement of the 1970's because now at the beginning of the twenty-first century there is more dialog between science and theology than there was even in the 1970's.[3] Currently there are thousands of creation-scientists who once again practice their scientific research in the clear light of the Biblical record.

God is Creator and Sustainer

The Bible reveals that a supernatural God not only is the Creator but also is the Sustainer of nature; and we learn from the New Testament that this God is Jesus Christ, God's Son. For example, see Colossians 1:16–17 where Christ is presented as the Creator and the one who holds all things together. In Hebrews 1:2–3 Christ is pictured as the Creator and as "sustaining all things by his powerful word."

Some people, who are known as deists, believe that God started the universe, established the laws of nature, and then withdrew to let the universe operate as a self-sustaining system. This would be like making a clock, winding it up, and then just letting it run down without any more attention. A serious problem with this deistic concept is that the Bible presents God not only as Creator but also as Sustainer, and if God is *only* the Creator He can become relatively unimportant to us on a daily basis.

Faith—Who Has It?

A reasonably broad definition of faith is "belief based upon limited evidence." So everybody lives throughout each day constantly demonstrating faith of one kind or another. When people get up in the morning they expect to see daylight because of their faith that the sun will show its light at a certain time. If you ask why they believe this, they may say they believe it because it happens every day and always has done so as far back as we know. But since the earth and the sun are not eternal, there was a time when neither the earth nor the sun existed.

We even expect that some time in the future our present conditions no longer will exist. But still people generally hold to the belief that there will be sunlight on the earth tomorrow. Although this belief is reasonable, it still is sustained by a type of faith. When we put a letter in the mailbox we also are exercising faith because sometimes letters do not arrive at their destination (Figure 9). In fact, all facets of our daily lives involve some aspects of "faith."

Figure 9. Every time a letter is mailed the mailer exercises a "faith" that it will arrive at its destination. Everybody, including scientists, operates on the basis of "faith." An atheist has "faith" that there is no God, but most people have faith in the supernatural God.

Figure 10. Philosophers tell us that we can not prove that we even exist. Maybe we are just part of a dream. Descartes answered this problem by saying that something had to be doubting its existence. Some "faith" still is required because the doubting still could be part of a dream. Also a person must have faith in the reasoning process. So some "faith" is involved in the life of everybody throughout the day.

A very basic and ancient question raised by philosophers involves the actuality of our very existence. They ask, "Do I exist?" Most people do not even think about such basic questions. But can you really prove that you exist? The answer is no! Perhaps you are just part of a big dream (which even could include dreaming about one or more dreams). The philosopher Descartes answered by saying that people believe (or have "faith") that they exist because they are able to think about this question, and so some existence has to be pondering this issue! His famous statement was, "I think. Therefore I am"—Figure 10. But, if you accept this argument ("I think. Therefore I am.") you still must have some *faith* in the validity of your thinking processes.

Scientists and Faith

Certain scientists have tried to convey the idea that they will believe only what can be demonstrated by science. This view is called "positivism." Those holding this position affirm that only the methods of science are valid for discovering truth in any field. For such people, science, which should be the servant of mankind, has become their "savior."

Some have gone so far as to reject God because they are not able to examine Him in their laboratory test tubes. It is reported that an atheist, Robert Ingersol, even challenged God, saying to Him, "If you exist, then strike me dead." This is like a young child saying to his father, "If you are my dad, prove it by killing me." But a good father would not be expected to take orders from his young child, and furthermore he loves the child and would not obey this request.

Like all other humans, scientists are exercising faith. They believe, for example, that the laws of nature, like gravity, will remain constant under given conditions. Scientists operate (as do all people) on the basis of causality, by believing that there are detectable causes for everything, such as for the dent in the fender of my car, or for my stomachache. Such belief (faith) in causality leads back ultimately to God as the first (ultimate) Cause and the Creator.

Faith of a "Non-Believer"

It requires faith for an atheist to say that there is no God. The atheist would be able to say there really is no god only after examining in the whole universe every place and condition under which God might exist. The atheist, therefore, also is living by a type of faith. Nobody is exempt from exercising faith which is belief based upon limited evidence.

If a scientist asserts that nature always has been here and therefore had no Creator, we must recognize that this assertion is a non-scientific statement. All persons affirming this in scientific fashion may have extended their thinking about causes back to the origin of our universe and even of matter and energy. But this person has stopped before the next logical scientific (that is, cause and effect) step of recognizing a supernatural power, and the person has expressed his faith in "no God." It is true that Christians and other theists have faith in God, but in coming to this faith in God, they actually go one logical causal step beyond that of the atheist.

Some folks, called agnostics, believe we do not know whether or not there is a supernatural God. This means that they just do not perceive whether God exists. Some extreme agnostics say that even if there is a God, nobody ever will be able to know about this existence. These extreme agnostics (along with some other agnostics, and, *even* some theists) are *practical atheists* because they live

Figure 11. There is revelation of God in nature, conscience, and history. All of these point to a supernatural God, but we need to know God personally. Many details about God and his will for us are revealed in the Bible. One of God's promises as found in Jeremiah 29:13 is, "You will seek me and find me when you seek me with all your heart."

as though God does not exist. We even may question whether these people seriously are concerned about God.

Nevertheless, we need to remember that not all agnostics and not all unbelievers are practical atheists. Some unbelievers truly want to know about God and to meet Him if that is possible. The prophet Jeremiah expressed well how honest seekers (including agnostics) can find God. In Jeremiah 29:13 the Lord declares that, "You will seek me and find me when you seek me with all your heart." This is God's promise; see Figure 11.

My Faith

For several years before I was a Christian, I was wondering, seeking, and even praying to a God I did not yet know personally. I was eighteen years old and in the United States Navy when another sailor one day explained to me from the Bible how to get right with God as a gift (grace) through faith in Jesus Christ. I knew deep within my soul that this was the answer to my quest.

This happened many years ago, and since that day I have lived with assurance of salvation as in I John 5:13 where it says that, "you may know that you have eternal life." I have had some doubts and many questions, especially after moving into a career in science. But over the years God has given me Christian friends, many of whom also were scientists, and they have helped me find answers to my questions concerning the Bible and science.

Most of my questions have been answered, but for some others I have not yet found final answers. There is a very comforting verse in I Corinthians 13:12 which says, "Now we see but a poor reflection; then we shall see face to face. Now I know in part; then I shall know fully, even as I am fully known." When I was in college I grasped the significance of the powerful truth in those words of I Corinthians 13:12. They seemed to say, "In this world you can live with some problems; it is OK because the answers all will be provided later in heaven."

People who believe the Bible and have a personal relationship with Jesus Christ, may not have *final answers* to all questions, but in virtually all cases they can obtain *logical and reasonable choices for answers*.

Seeing God in Relationship with the Creation

In discussing the relationship between God and His creation, the great Christian author, C. S. Lewis, has said that if we are looking to find God by studying an aspect of nature, this is like reading Shakespeare and trying to identify Shakespeare as *only one* of the characters in his stories! In reality, God is related to His universe as an author like Shakespeare is related to his plays. The author is expressed in all aspects of the productions just as our Creator-God is expressing Himself in every facet of nature. Even though some actors more directly may represent the person of the author, still the author cannot insert himself as *only one* of the characters.

For someone to know the author of a play or a book, however, there must be an introduction, a meeting. Any individual can recognize the handiwork of God throughout nature. However, the salvation experience which is by grace (a gift, or unmerited favor) through faith is vital before a person can commence a personal relationship with the Creator. See Ephesians 2:8–9 in the Bible. On a cross Jesus Christ died for us so that we, through forgiveness of our sins, can experience a close personal relationship with God. This message is what the Bible refers to as the "Gospel" which means "good news."

Genuine Biblical faith involves believing in God and that He has revealed Himself in nature, history, conscience, and (most intimately) in the Bible. Natural revelation declares God's power, but the Bible unveils our sinful (basically selfish) condition in the presence of a holy God. The Bible explains how we may accept the good news and live holy lives. Hebrews 11 in the Bible explains what faith is and provides historic examples of men and women who served God faithfully.

The Christian Church Set the Stage for Modern Science

It is very important to recognize that the birth of modern science occurred in Europe on a stage which had been set by the Christian church. If this is the case then why did not the scientific revolution eventuate about 1,600 years earlier when the church itself came into being? The answer is that even though the stage was there, the props and the actors were not yet ready. But the revolution which has led to the advanced state of science today did in fact occur in the region where Christianity was the dominant religion[4] (Figure 12). Many Greeks held to a belief in supernatural figures who behaved in unpredictable ways. But the Bible points to an orderly universe governed by a Creator/Sustainer-supernatural God.

> ...the scientific and technological revolutions first took place, and probably only could have first taken place [in Europe],

Figure 12. History shows that modern science developed "on a stage" which had been set by the Christian church. Christianity was the dominant religion in Europe where the scientific revolution occurred about 400 years ago.

where there was widespread confidence in the orderliness of the natural world.[5]

The method of investigation that we now know as modern science first emerged in Christianized Europe, a culture steeped in biblical faith, and most of the key figures in the scientific revolution were believers.[6]

The Bible in Psalm 24:1 tells us that "The earth is the Lord's, and everything in it, the world and all who live in it." The foundations for our modern science were laid by many scientists who were active outspoken Christians. Among these scientists were Johannes Kepler, Sir Isaac Newton (Figure 13), Michael Faraday, and Louis Agassiz. Francis Bacon (Figure 14), who is credited with giving us the scientific method, believed that we should study both the world of God (science) and the Word of God (Bible).

Figure 13. Sir Isaac Newton (1642–1727) was an English physicist and mathematician who laid foundations for modern physics. His contributions included calculus, and studies of gravity, motion, and optics. He recognized that his discoveries were made as answers to prayer, and he was in the habit of daily Bible study.

Figure 14. Francis Bacon, the Englishman credited with giving us the scientific method, said that we should study both the world of God (science) and the Word of God (Bible).

Sir Francis Bacon
(1561-1626)

These past scientists and many current scientists have understood that when they observed nature they were intensifying and broadening their understanding of the Creator-God and His work.[7] The Bible says to us, "The heavens declare the glory of God; the skies proclaim the work of his hands" (Psalm 19:1). We also are told to "Taste and see that the Lord is good; blessed is the man who takes refuge in Him" (Psalm 34:8).

The Christian Church Favors Good Science
Some have imagined that the Christian church as a whole has acted in opposition to science, but this has not been true. It certainly is true, however, that certain individuals within Christian-

ity have behaved improperly toward science. Some strong leaders who called themselves Christians have led groups astray into doctrines or actions that are not Biblical. This is why it is imperative that we maintain and propagate beliefs and actions that are based firmly upon Biblical principles.

A poll taken in late 1996 indicated that about forty percent of people in the scientific community believe in a prayer-answering God, and this apparently has been true for many years in the United States.[8] In public education today, however, it is common for science teachers to think of science and theology as two non-interacting realms. It is important that not only should we recognize science and theology as separate fields, but also we should remember and teach that they do have important relationships to each other. See Figure 8 (p. 26).

A logical extension of scientific cause and effect considerations points to a supernatural Creator whom we learn from revelation also is the Sustainer of all nature and is represented in the person of Jesus Christ. All persons live by a type of faith, and it is the object of our faith which is most important.

2

A Current Creationist View

What a Creationist Believes

The word "creation" comes from the Latin, and it means to produce. It is used in the sense of bringing something into existence, usually referring to God's activity. Creation is a clear and prominent Biblical doctrine. The first verse of the Bible says, "In the beginning God created the heavens and the earth" (Genesis 1:1). Throughout the Bible there are hundreds of other passages referring to creation, so anyone believing the Bible must believe in creation! Creation includes the belief that at the beginning a supernatural God created nature which basically consists of matter and energy. The Christian position is that before this *only* God existed, so this infinite God created the matter/energy from *nothing*.

The creation included the various elements like hydrogen, oxygen, sodium, iron, and gold. God created stars like our sun, wherein radiant energy is produced when hydrogen atoms join by twos to form single helium atoms (Figure15). Also, He created the earth, water, animals, plants, and our first parents. The Creator worked rapidly during the period of creation, and in six days He made many *kinds* (Hebrew *min*) of plants and animals separate from each other.

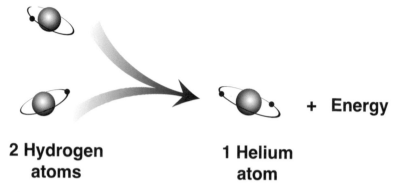

2 Hydrogen atoms   **1 Helium atom**   **+ Energy**

Figure 15. Nuclear fusion. When pairs of tiny hydrogen atoms join to form single helium atoms, considerable energy is released. It is believed that sunlight is produced from this process. The above simplified drawing "summarizes" a process involving several steps.

Included in nature are the laws of thermodynamics, gravity, and biogenesis. Nature has operated according to these basic creation laws, but it has taken humans many years to discover them. For instance, the law of biogenesis was not well-recognized until the late 1800's when it was realized that new organisms of any type come only by reproduction from other forms of that type.

Any moth comes specifically from the same type of parental moths. But just a few years ago some people still believed that fur coats actually could turn into moths. Although an observation of a coat in the closet might seem to support this conclusion, careful scientific studies have showed that adult moths laid eggs which hatched to become the larvas found eating the coat. A larva pupated, and at the appropriate time out came a moth which was like the parent which laid the original egg. This is just one of countless examples clearly demonstrating that every life form reproduces a similar life form—this concept being called the "law of biogenesis" as seen in Figure 2 (p. 17).

So God created nature with its laws, but the Bible also indicates that God still is involved, sustaining the universe He created. The supervisor of a factory does not just let the machinery run by itself. He carefully watches and controls every aspect of the operation so that it will continue to function efficiently.

However, if the workers do not perform their duties well, things can go wrong. For example, people have polluted their environments. Possibly, God may have allowed this to teach us some important lessons. In the grandest way God still is in constant control of the nature He created, and we as God's servants (based upon the best scientific knowledge) need to be responsible regarding environmental concerns. Even though God has authority over all aspects of nature, He has assigned to humans the jurisdiction over life on this planet (Genesis 1:26–29), this being a responsibility which individuals and their societies have not always accepted.[9]

The God of the Bible is represented as all powerful (omnipotent), knowing everything (omniscient), and being everywhere at the same time (omnipresent).

Miracles

Even though all of nature was created by God, nature is not the same as God. Nature consists of matter/energy, but God who is spirit (John 4:24) is *super*natural. This is the clear Biblical picture. However, there have been times when the Lord has chosen to act in ways that appear contrary to our human understanding of the laws of nature. These acts we term miracles, and they occurred, for example, when God made a dry path for the army of Israel to pass through the Red Sea with a wall of water on each side (Exodus 14:22).

Jesus Christ fed five thousand people starting with only five loaves of bread and two fishes (Luke 9:13–17). Where did He get the additional bread and fishes? We think the best understanding of this Biblical account is that Jesus Christ created them. He as Creator-God had the privilege of performing this miracle in order to demonstrate His own power. Jesus Christ was completely God and completely human at the same time. So this provision for the hungry people was motivated by His desire that God, not man, should receive the glory, and that people should believe in **Him**.

Types (Kinds)

So all creationists today believe that a supernatural God created living organisms. My understanding and that of other creation-scientists is that God created the different types of plants and animals, and none of these separate types physically is related to any other types. There have been limited changes within the types (as for humans, dogs or cats) but not crosses between the types. This typology (or limited change) view is modeled as a forest of trees (each tree representing a type). The trees lack roots because each type or kind started separately at its time of creation. Figure 16 shows a diagram of this model.

This view fits with what God reveals in Genesis 1 and 2. Also scientifically we observe that there are gaps between different types in the fossil record and among living types today. Many organisms appear abruptly as fossils in the rocks. The best example is in sedimentary rocks geologists call the Cambrian. This abrupt appearance and the universal gaps in the fossil record strongly suggest that God created separate kinds.

Many scientists have acknowledged the statistical impossibility of

Figure 16. The supernatural God designed and created the various "kinds" of plants and animals represented by a large forest of trees, a small portion of the forest being represented here. Each of the trees illustrates a kind or type and shows the variation or diversification which has occurred since the original creation. A species, whether it is living or extinct, would be at the tip of a branch. Many factors including genetic and environmental (catastrophes—fire, Flood, earthquake) would influence survival of the various species.

life's originating and even evolving by chance processes without the activity of God. The late Carl Sagan was an ardent evolutionist and anti-creationist, but he was aware of difficulties associated with his evolutionary beliefs. Starting with building blocks (nucleotides) of DNA he said, "a rough estimate of the genetic unlikelihood of a given human being" is roughly one chance in $10^{2,000,000,000}$ (that is, one chance out of 1 followed by two billion zeros).[10] For him the answer was darwinism, but based upon available facts creationists theorize that the human kind originated separately from all other types.

So creation-scientists affirm that their theory is superior to an evolutionary theory because the facts collected in a study of nature are more consistent with this creationist view.

Conclusion

So far we have discussed some basic ideas in order to lay a foundation for understanding science and theology. Also faith is very important, and Jesus Christ as God should be the main object of our faith in this twenty-first century. Likewise, it is important to realize that modern science was born in Europe where Christianity was the dominant religion.

Now we will turn the telescopes of our minds back to examine some historic thoughts about science and religion. In this panorama there is an emphasis upon origins, including creation and some early evolution ideas. We already have considered the modern creationist view of the creation of types, and now we will travel a portion of the historical pathway that has brought this position to popular public attention.

3

History of Creation-Evolution Thinking

Early History

The records of ancient peoples are filled with various legends dealing with the subject of origins and of various gods which were involved to one degree or another. Certain of these stories including the Babylonian Enuma Elish have some similarity to the Biblical account. This might be expected because God has given us in the Bible a creation report which spread to many different groups of people.

Historians of evolution have recognized some speculation and rash anticipations of evolutionary thinking as far back as the Greeks, about 600 B.C., when Thales, for example, speculated that everything came from water. A few years later, Anaximenes, a pupil of Anaximander proposed that life came from a mixture of earth and water (mud). He called the mixture "primordial terrestrial slime." In the sun's heat, plants and animals were produced; see Figure 17. This production of life from non-living material is termed abiogenesis. This opinion that life can come from some-

Figure 17. About 600 years B.C. the Grecian Anaximenes proposed a spontaneous generation scheme. He speculated that in the sun's heat plants and animals were produced from "primordial terrestrial slime" which was a mixture of earth and water.

thing not alive (also called spontaneous generation) was popular for more than two thousand years.

The greatest Greek scientist, Aristotle (384–322 B.C.), was another scholar who believed in abiogenesis. Also, he recognized that nature gave evidence of God's *intelligent design*. Interestingly, the Roman Augustine (353–430 A.D.) believed that God at one

Figure 18. A general schematic creationist depiction indicating that God created the various types (or kinds) of plants and animals fully-formed.

moment created all things as seeds which had the potential to develop.

Sixteenth and Seventeenth Centuries

The Spanish Jesuit theologian, Francisco Suarez (1548–1617), had very different views and has been called the "founder of special creation." The special creation concept includes the belief that the supernatural God designed and brought into being the various "kinds" of plants and animals as illustrated in Figure 18. Suarez reasoned that some original species could hybridize. For example, a mating between a female horse and a male donkey could lead to the birth of a mule. Usually these types of hybrids do not reproduce.

Francis Bacon (1561–1626, see Figure 14, p. 40), the Englishman well known for his promotion of the "scientific method," also believed that there had been some changes among species. Bacon encouraged a study of the Word of God (the Bible) and the work of God (the creation).

Eighteenth and Nineteenth Centuries

The famous Swedish scientist, Linnaeus (1707–1778, see Figure 19), also supported a belief that there had been modifications of the kinds or types originally created by God. From about 1550–1850 all theologians basically accepted special creation of the kinds or types, but the idea that there had been no changes in basic species ("fixity of species") certainly was not universally believed.

Some of the sixteenth- through nineteenth-century ideas clearly are consistent with the concept that there have been some changes ("limited changes") since the creation of the basic kinds (or types). Essentially, this is the most popular view held by creationists today.

An important forerunner of Charles Darwin was his grandfather, Erasmus Darwin (1731–1802). Especially late in his life, his ideas included a firm evolution, as from specks of life through a series to flying creatures, and of humans from some previous four-limbed creature (quadruped), possibly monkeys.

The very famous French naturalist, Lamarck (1744–1829), is best

Figure 19. The famous Swedish scientist, Linnaeus (1707–1778), gave us the biological scheme of classification which still is used today. He believed that there had been some modifications of the kinds or types originally created by God.

known for his promotion of the concept of inheritance of acquired adaptions. This perception is that some adjustments by living things over time would be passed to the offspring. For example, a man who had exercised to develop large muscles would have children with large muscles.

Another Frenchman, Geoffroy St. Hilaire (1772–1844), proposed big evolutionary jumps, for example that the first bird could hatch

"It's our new baby!"

Figure 20. The idea that a bird could hatch from a reptile egg is termed saltation. If this were possible it would be a huge jump from one type to another. There is no evidence that this sort of thing ever happened, and it is extremely unlikely that this could happen, because big changes almost always result in death for the offspring.

from an egg laid by a reptile—see Figure 20. This idea (known as saltation) also has been promoted in the twentieth century by certain scientists (for example Goldschmidt, Lovtrup, and Schindewolf).

It is important to recognize that in the 1850's there were several views available—(1) the idea that the species (or types) did not change, (2) the belief that the changes were small, or (3) the concept of those like Lamarck who thought that large changes had occurred in the past.

Charles Darwin (1809–1882) published the first edition of his most famous book, *The Origin of Species,* in 1859. He believed in a slow process of change which led to all forms of life. The most popular current evolution views basically are Darwinian.

The Twentieth—A Bloody Century

Between 1871 and 1914 there were no great wars affecting all civilization. So it was popular at the turn of the century to believe that humans had evolved to the point where they could learn to work together peacefully—discussing and solving their problems with no more wars, sharing the wealth, food for all, etc. This unrealistic perception of the "human creature" drastically was shattered by the horrors of two bloody twentieth-century World Wars.[11]

The realistic Christian understanding of the human condition is that all people on planet earth are sinners and will live basically selfish lives unless touched by the Spirit of the Living God. The only real solution to the basic human problem is personal salvation through Jesus Christ.

During early decades of the twentieth century some scientists who were Christians made some critical studies of evolution beliefs. The Bible-believing scientists who were engaged in these studies, along with scholars in other fields, had a concern to deal with the issues in an authoritative fashion. All of these efforts were com-

mendable, but they attracted little attention from the evolutionary community. However, they did provide a foundation for an
increasingly-popular perspective on origins.

Modern Creationist Movement

The modern creationist movement now is recognized as having
its beginning in 1961 after the publication of a book on *The Genesis Flood* authored by theologian John Whitcomb and scientist
Henry Morris.[12] In 1963 the Creation Research Society was orga-
nized and in 1964 commenced publication of a scientific journal
four times a year. It is called the *Creation Research Society Quarterly (CRSQ)*. Soon many dozens of creationist organizations burst
into being in the USA and many other countries including Australia, Germany, Korea, Russia, and Turkey. Now in the twenty-
first century there are many excellent periodicals (Figure 21),
books, and web sites presenting creationist views.

The Arkansas creation trial in December 1981 attracted extensive
media coverage which served to fuel interest in creationist activities.[13] Creationist ventures increased, including the initiation of
new scholarly publications. Many large creationist conferences were
held all over the country. In 1986, in Pittsburgh, Pennsylvania,
there was an international scientific creation conference, and it
has continued to meet at four-year intervals. These and many
other creationist endeavors have been led by members of the scientific community who had converted from an evolution to a
creation position.

It is important to repeat what is meant by the term creation. The
word creation may be utilized in a broad general sense, but as
used here it excludes theistic evolution, which is the view that

Figure 21. Some current creationist periodicals in English. Most of these are North American, but Australia and England also are represented. Nature Friend *is for children and* Creation Illustrated *has beautiful full-color illustrations and writeups for popular reading. Others are more scholarly. Addresses for all of these publications are listed at the back of this book.*

God created living things by using the process of evolution. In popular terminology of the past several decades the terms creation, creationist, and creationism mainly have been utilized with reference to the limited change model as seen in Figure 22. Since the 1960's those promoting the limited change model have been very active (meeting, publishing, debating evolutionists, etc.) and have attracted considerable attention. This creationist view con-

Figure 22. *In this very generalized creationist "forest" each tree represents a type or kind. There have been small changes within types, but not between or among them because no roots connect any type to any other type.*

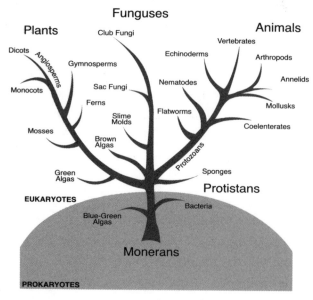

Figure 23. *The evolutionist "tree" illustrates the belief that all plants and animals would be related to all other plants and animals (including living and fossil forms).*

trasts with the evolution position that every form of life is related to every other form of life—see Figure 23.

Polls consistently have revealed that most people want both creation *and* evolution taught in public schools.[14] Some teachers have been presenting only creation or only evolution to their classes. But fortunately an increasing number of teachers, along with their students, are realizing the importance of knowing both views.

In this twenty-first century we anticipate many technological changes—new medical procedures, transportation including space travel, machinery (including computers in our homes), etc. But it is most important that people have the best philosophical foundation for living their lives. This foundation includes having an understanding of and possession of a personal relationship with the God of creation.

References and Notes

[1] Koestler, Arthur. 1959. *The sleepwalkers.* Macmillan, New York. pp. 537–539.

[2] Jastrow, Robert. 1978. *God and the astronomers.* W.W. Norton, New York. p. 116. For a discussion of the importance of God in modern science see Frair, Wayne. 1990. Second response to Robert C. Newman. pp. 439–451 *in* Kantzer, Kenneth S. and Carl F. H. Henry, eds. *Evangelical affirmations.* Zondervan Publishing House, Grand Rapids, Michigan. A more detailed recent treatment of science and theology is found in Geisler, Norman and Peter Bocchino. 2001. *Unshakable foundations: contemporary answers to crucial questions about the Christian faith.* Bethany House, Minneapolis, Minnesota.

[3] Easterbrook, Gregg. 1997. Science and God: a warming trend? *Science* 277:890–893.

[4] Hodgson, Peter. Undated. The Christian origin of science. *Occasional Papers Number 4.* The Farmington Institute for Christian Studies, 4 Park Town, Oxford (Tel: 0865 57456). 4 pp.; Jaki, Stanley L. 1974. *Science and creation.* Scottish Academic Press; Jaki, Stanley L. 1978. *The road of science and the ways to God.* Scottish Academic Press, 22 Hanover street, Edinburgh EH2 2EP Scotland, United Kingdom.

[5] Larson, David R. 2001. Larson made this comment in his commentary on a talk given 3 February 2001 by Phillip Johnson at Loma Linda in California. This quote was downloaded from *phylonews@uclink4.berkeley.edu* which had been posted on Monday 5 February 2001 at 1720 hours.

[6] Colson, Charles and Nancy Pearcey. 1999. *How now shall we live?* Tyndale House Publishers, Wheaton, Illinois. p. 422. Also see Pearcey, Nancy R. and Charles B. Thaxton. 1994. *The soul of science: Christian faith and natural philosophy.* Crossway, Wheaton, Illinois.

[7] Morris, Henry M. 1988. *Men of science——men of God: great scientists who believed the Bible,* second edition. Master Books, P.O. Box 727, Green Forest, Arkansas 72638. Another book dealing with scientists of the past is Lamont, Ann. 1995. *21 great scientists who believed the Bible.* Creation Science Foundation, P.O. Box 6302, Acacia Ridge D. C., Queensland 4110, Australia. A book with chapters written by living scientists is Ashton, John F., ed. 2000. *In six days: why fifty scientists choose to believe in creation.* Master Books, Green Forest, Arkansas.

[8] Larson, Edward L. and Larry Witham. 1997. Scientists are still keeping the faith. *Nature* 386:435–436.

[9] Pollution occurs because of one of the following factors: ignorance, inertia, or irresponsibility. See Frair, Wayne. 1969. Ignorance, inertia, and irresponsibility. *Journal of the American Scientific Affiliation* 21(2):43–44.

[10] Sagan, Carl. 1973. Extraterrestrial life. p. 46 *in* Sagan, Carl, ed. *Communications with extraterrestrial intelligence.* MIT Press, Cambridge, Massachusetts.

[11] This material was obtained by personal communication from historian Howard F. Vos.

[12] Whitcomb, John C. and Henry M. Morris. 1961. *The Genesis Flood: the Biblical record and its scientific implications.* Presbyterian and Reformed Publishing Company, Nutley, New Jersey. (Now obtainable from the Institute for Creation Research, P.O. Box 2667, El Cajon, California 92021.)

[13] Frair, Wayne. 1998. Effects of the 1981 Arkansas trial on the creationist movement. pp. 229–239 *in* Walsh, Robert E, ed. *Proceedings of the Fourth International Conference on Creationism.* 3–8 August 1998. Technical Symposium Sessions. Creation Science Fellowship, P.O. Box 99303, Pittsburgh, Pennsylvania 15233-4303.

[14] Glanz, James. 2000. Survey finds support is strong for teaching two Origin theories. *The New York Times* Saturday, 11 March 2000:A1, A10.

Glossary

Abiogenesis — Synonym for spontaneous generation.

Biogenesis — The scientific law that every living thing has come from a similar type of life.

Creation — The view that the supernatural God formed from nothing the universe including life on earth.

Energy — The capacity to do work.

Evolution — Briefly can refer to "change." The most popular use of the term refers to darwinism, which is the theory that all forms of life are related, and have been produced by natural processes leading to the accumulation of small changes during long periods of time.

Faith — Belief based upon limited evidence.

Hypothesis — The earliest form of a conclusion based on available evidence.

Intelligent design — A conclusion that thinking ability and creative skill were involved in making objects having order and useful purpose.

Law	A well-established scientific concept, for example the law of gravity.
Life	Matter having the capacity to metabolize and reproduce.
Limited change model	The view that God created unrelated types (kinds) of living things which have varied within boundaries. Types appear abruptly in the fossil record.
Matter	The material composing nature.
Metabolism	Within living cells, an association of chemical processes which utilize energy and produce waste.
Miracle	Supernatural event for which there is no "natural" explanation.
Model	A representation of an object or event.
Natural science	Knowledge of and a study of nature.
Nature	Anything in the universe including stars, trees, animals, rocks, air, etc.
Natural revelation	In nature the expression of information about the character of God.
Revelation	God's communication in nature, history, conscience, and in the Bible.

Science | Knowledge about and methods for studying nature or some other field of interest.

Spontaneous generation | Outdated hypothesis that some non-living matter could become alive.

Theology | Study of God (supernatural power) and God's relation to nature (the creation).

Theory | A conclusion which is better established than a hypothesis.

Typology | See limited change model.

Some Creationist Periodicals

Acts & Facts
Institute for Creation Research
P.O. Box 2667
El Cajon, California 92021
Popular free monthly discussing creationist issues.
www.icr.org

Creation Illustrated
Creation Illustrated Subscription Services
P.O. Box 469119
Escondido, California 92046-9119
Full color and popular.
www.creationillustrated.com

Creation Research Society Quarterly (CRSQ)
Creation Research Society
P.O. Box 8263
St. Joseph, Missouri 64508-8263
Technical with some popular material.
www.creationresearch.org

Creation
Answers in Genesis
P.O. Box 6330
Florence, Kentucky 41022
Some technical material and some written in popular style.
www.AnswersinGenesis.org

CREATION:
The Journal of the Creation Science Movement
P.O. Box 888
Portsmouth P06 2YD, United Kingdom
British, popular and some technical.
www.creationsciencemovement.com

Dialogue
Creation Science Association of Alberta
5328 Calgary Trail South, Suite 1136
Edmonton, Alberta, T6H 4J8, Canada
Semi-popular and authoritatively written.

Discovery: Scripture and Science for Kids
Apologetics Press
230 Landmark Drive
Montgomery, Alabama 36117
Popular (color) monthly for children especially from
8–12 years old.
www.DiscoveryMagazine.com

Nature Friend
2673 TR 421
Sugarcreek, Ohio 44681
In color, a nature and creationist monthly
written for children 4-14 years old.
Nature's Workshop Plus science catalog.
www.naturesworkshopplus.com

Origins and Design
Access Research Network
P.O. Box 38069
Colorado Springs, Colorado 80937-8069
Scholarly and popular.
www.arn.org

Origins
Geoscience Research Institute
Loma Linda University
Loma Linda, California 92350
Primarily technical.

Origins Insights
Creation Science Fellowship
P.O. Box 99303
Pittsburgh, Pennsylvania 15233-4303
This monthly technical/popular organ represents many other
smaller publications from specific local creationist groups. The
CSF in Pittsburgh has sponsored quadrennial international
scientific creation conferences since 1986.
www.csfpittsburgh.org

Reason and Revelation
Apologetics Press
230 Landmark Drive
Montgomery, Alabama 36117
Discussions of many theological and scientific issues.
www.ApologeticsPress.org

Technical Journal (recently changed name to *TJ*)
Answers in Genesis
P.O. Box 6330
Florence, Kentucky 41022
Technical with some popular material.
www.AnswersinGenesis.org

Books for Further Reading

Ashton, John F. 2000. *In six days: why fifty scientists choose to believe in creation.* Master Books, Green Forest, Arkansas.

Batten, Don (editor), Ken Ham, Jonathan Sarfati and Carl Wieland. 2000. *The revised & expanded answers book.* Master Books, Green Forest, Arkansas.

Bohlin, Ray. 2000. *Creation, evolution, & modern science.* Kregel Publications, Grand Rapids, Michigan.

Dembski, William A. and James M. Kushiner, editors. 2001. *Signs of intelligence: understanding intelligent design.* Baker Book House, Grand Rapids, Michigan.

Frair, Wayne F. and Percival Davis.1983. *A case for creation.* third edition. School of Tomorrow, Lewisville, Texas.

Gish, Duane T. 1990. *The amazing story of creation from science and the Bible.* Institute for Creation Research, El Cajon, California.

Hunter, Cornelius G. 2001. *Darwin's God: evolution and the problem of evil.* Baker Book House, Grand Rapids, Michigan.

Johnson, Phillip E. 2000. *The wedge of truth: splitting the foundation of materialism.* Intervarsity Press, Downers Grove, Illinois.

Morris, Henry M. and Gary E. Parker. 1987. *What is creation science?* revised edition. Institute for Creation Research, El Cajon, California.

Osborn, Henry Fairfield. 1929. *From the Greeks to Darwin, the development of the evolution idea through twenty-four centuries.* second edition. Charles Scribner's Sons, New York.

Perloff, James. 1999. *Tornado in a junkyard; the relentless myth of darwinism.* Refuge Books, Arlington, Massachusetts.

Roth, Ariel A. 1998. *Origins: linking science and Scripture.* Review and Herald Publishing, Hagerstown, Maryland.

Sarfati, Jonathan D. 1999. *Refuting evolution: a handbook for students, parents and teachers countering the latest arguments for evolution.* Master Books, Green Forest, Arkansas.

Wells, Jonathan. 2000. *Icons of evolution: science or myth? why much of what we teach about evolution is wrong.* Intervarsity Press, Downers Grove, Illinois.

Index

(continues, next page)

(continued from page 79)

Designs and Origins in Astronomy, edited by George Mulfinger, M.S.

Field Studies in Catastrophic Geology, by Carl R. Froede, Jr., P.G.

The North American Midcontinent Rift System, by John K. Reed, Ph.D.

The Human Body: An Intelligent Design, by Alan L. Gillen, Ed.D., Frank J. Sherwin III, M.A., and Alan Knowles, M.S.

Plate Tectonics: A Different View, edited by John K. Reed, Ph.D.

Natural History in the Christian Worldview, by John K. Reed, Ph.D.

For more information about the
Creation Research Society and a subscription
to the *Creation Research Society Quarterly*, write:
Membership Secretary
Creation Research Society
P.O. Box 8263
St. Joseph, MO 64508-8263